DIARY 2021

KU-350-135

JANUARY

M	T	W	T	F	S	S
				01		
04	05	06	07	08	0	
11	12	13	14	15	16	17
18	19	20	21	22	23	24
25	26	27	28	29	30	31

FEBRUARY

M	T	W	T	F	S	S
15	16	17	18	19	20	21
22	23	24	25	26	27	28

MARCH

M	T	W	T	F	S	S
						7
						4
15	16	17	18	19	20	21
22	23	24	25	26	27	28
29	30	31				

APRIL

M	T	W	T	F	S	S
			01	02	03	04
05	06	07	08	09	10	11
12	13	14	15	16	17	18
19	20	21	22	23	24	25
26	27	28	29	30		

MAY

M	T	W	T	F	S	S
					01	02
03	04	05	06	07	08	09
10	11	12	13	14	15	16
17	18	19	20	21	22	23
24	25	26	27	28	29	30
31						

JUNE

M	T	W	T	F	S	S
	01	02	03	04	05	06
07	08	09	10	11	12	13
14	15	16	17	18	19	20
21	22	23	24	25	26	27
28	29	30				

JULY

M	T	W	T	F	S	S
			01	02	03	04
05	06	07	08	09	10	11
12	13	14	15	16	17	18
19	20	21	22	23	24	25
26	27	28	29	30	31	

AUGUST

M	T	W	T	F	S	S
						01
02	03	04	05	06	07	08
09	10	11	12	13	14	15
16	17	18	19	20	21	22
23	24	25	26	27	28	29
30	31					

SEPTEMBER

M	T	W	T	F	S	S
		01	02	03	04	05
06	07	08	09	10	11	12
13	14	15	16	17	18	19
20	21	22	23	24	25	26
27	28	29	30			

OCTOBER

M	T	W	T	F	S	S
				01	02	03
04	05	06	07	08	09	10
11	12	13	14	15	16	17
18	19	20	21	22	23	24
25	26	27	28	29	30	31

NOVEMBER

M	T	W	T	F	S	S
01	02	03	04	05	06	07
08	09	10	11	12	13	14
15	16	17	18	19	20	21
22	23	24	25	26	27	28
29	30					

DECEMBER

M	T	W	T	F	S	S
		01	02	03	04	05
06	07	08	09	10	11	12
13	14	15	16	17	18	19
20	21	22	23	24	25	26
27	28	29	30	31		

2021 PLANNER

JANUARY	FEBRUARY	MARCH
01 F	01 M	01 M
02 S	02 T	02 T
03 S	03 W	03 W
04 M	04 T	04 T
05 T	05 F	05 F
06 W	06 S	06 S
07 T	07 S	07 S
08 F	08 M	08 M
09 S	09 T	09 T
10 S	10 W	10 W
11 M	11 T	11 T
12 T	12 F	12 F
13 W	13 S	13 S
14 T	14 S	14 S
15 F	15 M	15 M
16 S	16 T	16 T
17 S	17 W	17 W
18 M	18 T	18 T
19 T	19 F	19 F
20 W	20 S	20 S
21 T	21 S	21 S
22 F	22 M	22 M
23 S	23 T	23 T
24 S	24 W	24 W
25 M	25 T	25 T
26 T	26 F	26 F
27 W	27 S	27 S
28 T	28 S	28 S
29 F		29 M
30 S		30 T
31 S		31 W

2021 PLANNER

APRIL	MAY	JUNE
01 T	01 S	01 T
02 F	02 S	02 W
03 S	03 M	03 T
04 S	04 T	04 F
05 M	05 W	05 S
06 T	06 T	06 S
07 W	07 F	07 M
08 T	08 S	08 T
09 F	09 S	09 W
10 S	10 M	10 T
11 S	11 T	11 F
12 M	12 W	12 S
13 T	13 T	13 S
14 W	14 F	14 M
15 T	15 S	15 T
16 F	16 S	16 W
17 S	17 M	17 T
18 S	18 T	18 F
19 M	19 W	19 S
20 T	20 T	20 S
21 W	21 F	21 M
22 T	22 S	22 T
23 F	23 S	23 W
24 S	24 M	24 T
25 S	25 T	25 F
26 M	26 W	26 S
27 T	27 T	27 S
28 W	28 F	28 M
29 T	29 S	29 T
30 F	30 S	30 W
	31 M	

2021 PLANNER

JULY	AUGUST	SEPTEMBER
01 T	01 S	01 W
02 F	02 M	02 T
03 S	03 T	03 F
04 S	04 W	04 S
05 M	05 T	05 S
06 T	06 F	06 M
07 W	07 S	07 T
08 T	08 S	08 W
09 F	09 M	09 T
10 S	10 T	10 F
11 S	11 W	11 S
12 T	12 T	12 S
13 W	13 F	13 M
14 T	14 S	14 T
15 F	15 S	15 W
16 F	16 M	16 T
17 S	17 T	17 F
18 S	18 W	18 S
19 T	19 T	19 S
20 W	20 F	20 M
21 T	21 S	21 T
22 F	22 S	22 W
23 F	23 M	23 T
24 S	24 T	24 F
25 S	25 W	25 S
26 T	26 T	26 S
27 W	27 F	27 M
28 T	28 S	28 T
29 F	29 S	29 W
30 F	30 M	30 T
31 S	31 T	

2021 PLANNER

OCTOBER	NOVEMBER	DECEMBER
01 F	01 M	01 W
02 S	02 T	02 T
03 S	03 W	03 F
04 M	04 T	04 S
05 T	05 F	05 S
06 W	06 S	06 M
07 T	07 S	07 T
08 F	08 M	08 W
09 S	09 T	09 T
10 S	10 W	10 F
11 M	11 T	11 S
12 T	12 F	12 S
13 W	13 S	13 M
14 T	14 S	14 T
15 F	15 M	15 W
16 S	16 T	16 T
17 S	17 W	17 F
18 M	18 T	18 S
19 T	19 F	19 S
20 W	20 S	20 M
21 T	21 S	21 T
22 F	22 M	22 W
23 S	23 T	23 T
24 S	24 W	24 F
25 M	25 T	25 S
26 T	26 F	26 S
27 W	27 S	27 M
28 T	28 S	28 T
29 F	29 M	29 W
30 S	30 T	30 T
31 S		31 F

2021 NOTABLE DATES

JAN
01	FRI	NEW YEAR'S DAY
04	MON	2ND JANUARY [SUBSTITUTE DAY] (SCOTLAND); DAY AFTER NEW YEAR'S DAY [OBSERVED] (NZ)
06	WED	EPIPHANY
18	MON	MARTIN LUTHER KING DAY (USA)
25	MON	BURNS NIGHT (SCOTLAND)
26	TUES	AUSTRALIA DAY
28	THURS	TU B'SHEVAT (ARBOR DAY)

FEB
06	SAT	WAITANGI DAY (NZ)
08	MON	WAITANGI DAY [OBSERVED] (NZ)
12	FRI	CHINESE NEW YEAR (YEAR OF THE OX)
14	SUN	VALENTINE'S DAY
15	MON	PRESIDENTS' DAY (USA)
16	TUES	SHROVE TUESDAY
17	WED	ASH WEDNESDAY
26	FRI	PURIM

MAR
01	MON	ST DAVID'S DAY (WALES)
11	THURS	MAHA SHIVARATRI; ISRA AND MI'RAJ
14	SUN	MOTHERS'S DAY
17	WED	ST PATRICK'S DAY (N.IRELAND & ROI)
20	SAT	VERNAL EQUINOX
28	SUN	PALM SUNDAY; FIRST DAY OF PASSOVER; BRITISH SUMMER TIME BEGINS
29	MON	HOLI

APR
01	THURS	MAUNDY THURSDAY
02	FRI	GOOD FRIDAY
03	SAT	HOLY SATURDAY
04	SUN	EASTER SUNDAY; LAST DAY OF PASSOVER
05	MON	EASTER MONDAY (UK, ROI, CAN, AUS, NZ)
08	THURS	YOM HASHOAH
13	TUES	RAMADAN STARTS
15	THURS	YOM HAATZMAUT
23	FRI	ST GEORGE'S DAY; SHAKESPEARE DAY
25	SUN	ANZAC DAY (AUS, NZ)
26	MON	ANZAC DAY [OBSERVED] (AUS, NZ)
30	FRI	LAG B'OMER

MAY
03	MON	MAY BANK HOLIDAY (UK & ROI)
08	SAT	LAYLATUL QADR (NIGHT OF POWER)
13	THURS	ASCENSION DAY; EID AL-FITR
17	MON	SHAVUOT
23	SUN	PENTECOST
24	MON	WHIT MONDAY; VICTORIA DAY (CAN)
30	SUN	TRINITY SUNDAY
31	MON	SPRING BANK HOLIDAY (UK & ROI); MEMORIAL DAY (USA)

JUN
03	THURS	CORPUS CHRISTI
07	MON	JUNE BANK HOLIDAY (ROI); QUEEN'S BIRTHDAY (NZ)
12	SAT	QUEEN'S OFFICIAL BIRTRHDAY (UK)
20	SUN	FATHER'S DAY
21	MON	SUMMER SOLSTICE (UK)
22	TUES	WINDRUSH DAY
26	SAT	ARMED FORCES DAY (UK)

2021 NOTABLE DATES

JUL	01 THURS	CANADA DAY (CAN)
	04 SUN	INDEPENDENCE DAY (USA)
	05 MON	INDEPENDENCE DAY (USA) [OBSERVED]
	12 MON	BATTLE OF THE BOYNE DAY (N.IRELAND)
	18 SUN	TISHA B'AV
	20 TUES	EID UL ADHA

AUG	02 MON	SUMMER BANK HOLIDAY (SCOTLAND, ROI)
	10 TUES	MUHARRAM (ISLAMIC NEW YEAR)
	15 SUN	ASSUMPTION OF MARY
	19 THURS	ASHURA
	22 SUN	RAKSHA BANDHAN
	30 MON	SUMMER BANK HOLIDAY (UK EXCEPT SCOTLAND); JANMASHTAMI

SEP	06 MON	LABOR DAY (USA, CAN)
	07 TUES	ROSH HASHANA
	10 FRI	GANESH CHATURTHI
	16 THURS	YOM KIPPUR
	21 TUES	FIRST DAY OF SUKKOT
	22 WED	SEPTEMBER EQUINOX
	27 MON	HOSHANA RABBAH
	28 TUES	SHEMINI ATZERET
	29 WED	SIMCHAT TORAH

OCT	04 MON	FEAST OF ST FRANCIS OF ASSISI
	07 THURS	NAVARATRI
	11 MON	COLUMBUS DAY (USA); THANKSGIVING DAY (CAN)
	14 THURS	DUSSEHRA
	19 TUES	MILAD UN NABI (MAWLID)
	25 MON	OCTOBER BANK HOLIDAY (ROI); LABOUR DAY (NZ)
	31 SUN	BRITISH SUMMER TIME ENDS; HALLOWEEN

NOV	01 MON	ALL SAINTS' DAY
	02 TUES	ALL SOULS' DAY
	04 THURS	DIWALI/DEEPAVALI
	05 FRI	GUY FAWKES NIGHT
	11 THURS	VETERANS DAY (USA); REMEMBRANCE DAY (CAN)
	14 SUN	REMEMBRANCE SUNDAY
	25 THURS	THANKSGIVING DAY (USA)
	28 SUN	FIRST SUNDAY OF ADVENT
	29 MON	FIRST DAY OF HANUKKAH
	30 TUES	ST ANDREW'S DAY (SCOTLAND)

DEC	06 MON	LAST DAY OF HANUKKAH
	08 WED	FEAST OF THE IMMACULATE CONCEPTION
	21 TUES	DECEMBER SOLSTICE
	24 FRI	CHRISTMAS EVE; CHRISTMAS DAY [SUBSTITUTE DAY] (USA)
	25 SAT	CHRISTMAS DAY
	26 SUN	BOXING DAY; ST. STEPHEN'S DAY (ROI)
	27 MON	CHRISTMAS DAY [SUBSTITUTE DAY] (UK, CAN, AUS & NZ)
	28 TUES	BOXING DAY [SUBSTITUTE DAY] (UK, AUS & NZ)
	31 FRI	NEW YEAR'S EVE; NEW YEAR'S DAY [SUBSTITUTE DAY] (USA)

GENERAL INFORMATION

Imperial to Metric - 1 inch = 25.40 millimetres, 1 millimetre = 0.039 inches

To convert	Multiply by	To convert	Multiply by
Inches to Centimetres	2.5400	Cubic Centimetres to Cubic Inches	0.0610
Centimetres to Inches	0.3937	Cubic Feet to Cubic Metres	0.0283
Feet to Metres	0.3048	Cubic Metres to Cubic Feet	35.3100
Metres to Feet	3.2810	Cubic Yards to Cubic Metres	0.7646
Yards to Metres	0.9144	Cubic Metres to Cubic Yards	1.3080
Metres to Yards	1.0940	Cubic Inches to Litres	0.0163
Miles to Kilometres	1.6090	Litres to Cubic Inches	61.0300
Kilometres to Miles	0.6214	Gallons to Litres	4.5460
Sq Inches to Sq Centimetres	6.4520	Litres to Gallons	0.2200
Sq Centimetres to Sq Inches	0.1550	Grains to Grams	0.0648
Sq Metres to Sq Feet	10.7600	Grams to Grains	15.4300
Sq Feet to Sq Metres	0.0929	Ounces to Grams	28.3500
Sq Yards to Sq Metres	0.8361	Grams to Ounces	0.0352
Sq Metres to Sq Yards	1.1960	Pounds to Grams	453.6600
Sq Miles to Sq Kilometres	2.5900	Grams to Pounds	0.0022
Sq Kilometres to Sq Miles	0.3861	Pounds to Kilograms	0.4536
Acres to Hectares	0.4047	Kilograms to Pounds	2.2050
Hectares to Acres	2.4710	Tons to Kilograms	1014.000
Cubic Inches to Cubic Centimetres	16.3900	Kilograms to Tons	0.0009

World Times based on GMT at 12:00 hours compared with Local Standard Time

Algeria	GMT + 1	India	GMT + 5.5	Philippines	GMT + 8
Argentina	GMT - 3	Indonesia	GMT + 7	Poland	GMT + 1
Australia	GMT + 10	Iran	GMT + 3	Portugal	GMT
Austria	GMT + 1	Iraq	GMT + 3	Qatar	GMT + 3
Bahrain	GMT + 3	Ireland (Eire)	GMT	Romania	GMT + 2
Belgium	GMT + 1	Israel	GMT + 2	Russia	GMT + 3
Brazil	GMT - 3	Italy	GMT + 1	Saudi Arabia	GMT + 3
Bulgaria	GMT + 2	Japan	GMT + 9	Singapore	GMT + 8
Canada	GMT - 5	Kuwait	GMT + 3	South Africa	GMT + 2
Chile	GMT - 4	Lebanon	GMT + 2	Spain	GMT + 1
China	GMT + 8	Libya	GMT + 2	Sri Lanka	GMT + 5.5
Czech Rep.	GMT + 1	Luxembourg	GMT + 1	Sweden	GMT + 1
Denmark	GMT + 1	Malaysia	GMT + 8	Switzerland	GMT + 1
Egypt	GMT + 2	Mexico	GMT - 7	Syrian Rep.	GMT + 2
Finland	GMT + 2	Morocco	GMT	Taiwan	GMT + 8
France	GMT + 1	Netherlands	GMT + 1	Thailand	GMT + 7
Germany	GMT + 1	New Zealand	GMT + 12	Turkey	GMT + 2
Greece	GMT + 2	Nigeria	GMT + 1	UAE	GMT + 4
Hungary	GMT + 1	Norway	GMT + 1	UK	GMT
Iceland	GMT	Pakistan	GMT + 5.5	USA	GMT - 5

NEW YEARS EVE

THURSDAY 31

NEW YEAR'S DAY

FRIDAY 01

SATURDAY 02

SUNDAY 03

JANUARY
WEEK 01

04 MONDAY

2ND JANUARY [SUBSTITUTE DAY] (SCOTLAND):
DAY AFTER NEW YEAR'S DAY [OBSERVED] (NZ)

05 TUESDAY

06 WEDNESDAY EPIPHANY

THURSDAY 07

FRIDAY 08

SATURDAY 09

SUNDAY 10

11 MONDAY

12 TUESDAY

13 WEDNESDAY

THURSDAY 14

FRIDAY 15

SATURDAY 16

SUNDAY 17

18 MONDAY

MARTIN LUTHER KING DAY (USA)

19 TUESDAY

20 WEDNESDAY

THURSDAY 21

FRIDAY 22

SATURDAY 23

SUNDAY 24

JANUARY
WEEK 04

25 MONDAY — BURNS NIGHT (SCOTLAND)

26 TUESDAY — AUSTRALIA DAY

27 WEDNESDAY

TU B'SHEVAT (ARBOR DAY)

THURSDAY 28

FRIDAY 29

SATURDAY 30

SUNDAY 31

FEBRUARY
WEEK 05

01 MONDAY

02 TUESDAY

03 WEDNESDAY

THURSDAY   04

FRIDAY   05

WAITANGI DAY (NZ)   SATURDAY   06

SUNDAY   07

FEBRUARY
WEEK 06

08 MONDAY
WAITANGI DAY [OBSERVED] (NZ)

09 TUESDAY

10 WEDNESDAY

THURSDAY 11

CHINESE NEW YEAR (YEAR OF THE OX)

FRIDAY 12

SATURDAY 13

VALENTINE'S DAY

SUNDAY 14

FEBRUARY
WEEK 07

15 MONDAY PRESIDENTS' DAY (USA)

16 TUESDAY SHROVE TUESDAY

17 WEDNESDAY ASH WEDNESDAY

THURSDAY 18

FRIDAY 19

SATURDAY 20

SUNDAY 21

FEBRUARY
WEEK 08

22 MONDAY

23 TUESDAY

24 WEDNESDAY

THURSDAY 25

PURIM

FRIDAY 26

SATURDAY 27

SUNDAY 28

MARCH
WEEK 09

01 MONDAY   ST DAVID'S DAY (WALES)

02 TUESDAY

03 WEDNESDAY

THURSDAY 04

FRIDAY 05

SATURDAY 06

SUNDAY 07

08 MONDAY

09 TUESDAY

10 WEDNESDAY

MAHA SHIVARATRI; ISRA AND MI'RAJ

THURSDAY 11

FRIDAY 12

SATURDAY 13

MOTHER'S DAY

SUNDAY 14

MARCH
WEEK 11

15 MONDAY

16 TUESDAY

17 WEDNESDAY ST PATRICK'S DAY (N.IRELAND & ROI)

THURSDAY 18

FRIDAY 19

VERNAL EQUINOX

SATURDAY 20

SUNDAY 21

MARCH

22 MONDAY

23 TUESDAY

24 WEDNESDAY

THURSDAY 25

FRIDAY 26

SATURDAY 27

PALM SUNDAY; FIRST DAY OF PASSOVER;
BRITISH SUMMER TIME BEGINS

SUNDAY 28

MARCH
WEEK 13

29 MONDAY HOLI

30 TUESDAY

31 WEDNESDAY

MAUNDY THURSDAY · THURSDAY 01

GOOD FRIDAY · FRIDAY 02

HOLY SATURDAY · SATURDAY 03

EASTER SUNDAY: LAST DAY OF PASSOVER · SUNDAY 04

APRIL
WEEK 14

05 MONDAY EASTER MONDAY (UK, ROI, CAN, AUS, NZ)

06 TUESDAY

07 WEDNESDAY

YOM HASHOAH

THURSDAY 08

FRIDAY 09

SATURDAY 10

SUNDAY 11

12 MONDAY

13 TUESDAY   RAMADAN STARTS

14 WEDNESDAY

APRIL
WEEK 15

YOM HAATZMAUT

THURSDAY 15

FRIDAY 16

SATURDAY 17

SUNDAY 18

19 MONDAY

20 TUESDAY

21 WEDNESDAY

THURSDAY 22

ST GEORGE'S DAY; SHAKESPEARE DAY | FRIDAY 23

SATURDAY 24

ANZAC DAY (AUS, NZ) | SUNDAY 25

APRIL
WEEK 17

26 MONDAY
ANZAC DAY [OBSERVED] (AUS, NZ)

27 TUESDAY

28 WEDNESDAY

THURSDAY 29

LAG B'OMER

FRIDAY 30

SATURDAY 01

SUNDAY 02

MAY
WEEK 18

03 MONDAY   MAY BANK HOLIDAY (UK & ROI)

04 TUESDAY

05 WEDNESDAY

THURSDAY 06

FRIDAY 07

LAYLATUL QADR (NIGHT OF POWER)   SATURDAY 08

SUNDAY 09

MAY
WEEK 19

10 MONDAY

11 TUESDAY

12 WEDNESDAY

MAY
WEEK 19

ASCENSION DAY: EID AL-FITR

THURSDAY 13

FRIDAY 14

SATURDAY 15

SUNDAY 16

MAY
WEEK 20

17 MONDAY
SHAVUOT

18 TUESDAY

19 WEDNESDAY

THURSDAY 20

FRIDAY 21

SATURDAY 22

PENTECOST

SUNDAY 23

MAY
WEEK 21

24 MONDAY
WHIT MONDAY: VICTORIA DAY (CAN)

25 TUESDAY

26 WEDNESDAY

THURSDAY 27

FRIDAY 28

SATURDAY 29

TRINITY SUNDAY

SUNDAY 30

MAY
WEEK 22

JUNE
WEEK 22

31 MONDAY

SPRING BANK HOLIDAY (UK & ROI);
MEMORIAL DAY (USA)

01 TUESDAY

02 WEDNESDAY

CORPUS CHRISTI

THURSDAY 03

FRIDAY 04

SATURDAY 05

SUNDAY 06

JUNE
WEEK 23

07 MONDAY JUNE BANK HOLIDAY (ROI); QUEEN'S BIRTHDAY (NZ)

08 TUESDAY

09 WEDNESDAY

THURSDAY 10

FRIDAY 11

QUEEN'S OFFICIAL BIRTRHDAY (UK)

SATURDAY 12

SUNDAY 13

14 MONDAY

15 TUESDAY

16 WEDNESDAY

THURSDAY 17

FRIDAY 18

SATURDAY 19

FATHER'S DAY

SUNDAY 20

JUNE
WEEK 25

21 MONDAY   SUMMER SOLSTICE (UK)

22 TUESDAY   WINDRUSH DAY

23 WEDNESDAY

THURSDAY 24

FRIDAY 25

ARMED FORCES DAY (UK

SATURDAY 26

SUNDAY 27

JUNE
WEEK 26

28 MONDAY

29 TUESDAY

30 WEDNESDAY

JULY
WEEK 26

CANADA DAY (CAN)

THURSDAY 01

FRIDAY 02

SATURDAY 03

INDEPENDENCE DAY (USA)

SUNDAY 04

A year since meeting
culy

JULY
WEEK 27

05 MONDAY INDEPENDENCE DAY (USA) [OBSERVED]

06 TUESDAY

Leaving on holiday

07 WEDNESDAY

THURSDAY 08

FRIDAY 09

SATURDAY 10

SUNDAY 11

JULY
WEEK 28

12 MONDAY BATTLE OF THE BOYNE DAY (N.IRELAND)

13 TUESDAY

14 WEDNESDAY

THURSDAY 15

FRIDAY 16

SATURDAY 17

TISHA B'AV | SUNDAY 18

A year since I got
Caly

JULY
WEEK 29

19 MONDAY

20 TUESDAY   EID UL ADHA

21 WEDNESDAY

THURSDAY 22

FRIDAY 23

SATURDAY 24

SUNDAY 25

26 MONDAY

27 TUESDAY

28 WEDNESDAY

THURSDAY   29

FRIDAY   30

SATURDAY   31

SUNDAY   01

AUGUST
WEEK 31

02 MONDAY   SUMMER BANK HOLIDAY (SCOTLAND, ROI)

03 TUESDAY

04 WEDNESDAY

THURSDAY 05

FRIDAY 06

SATURDAY 07

SUNDAY 08

AUGUST
WEEK 32

09 MONDAY

10 TUESDAY   MUHARRAM (ISLAMIC NEW YEAR)

11 WEDNESDAY

THURSDAY 12

FRIDAY 13

SATURDAY 14

ASSUMPTION OF MARY | SUNDAY 15

AUGUST
WEEK 33

16 MONDAY

17 TUESDAY

18 WEDNESDAY

ASHURA

THURSDAY 19

FRIDAY 20

SATURDAY 21

RAKSHA BANDHAN

SUNDAY 22

AUGUST
WEEK 34

23 MONDAY

24 TUESDAY

25 WEDNESDAY

THURSDAY 26

FRIDAY 27

SATURDAY 28

SUNDAY 29

AUGUST
WEEK 35

SEPTEMBER
WEEK 35

30 MONDAY   SUMMER BANK HOLIDAY (UK EXCEPT SCOTLAND); JANMASHTAMI

31 TUESDAY

01 WEDNESDAY

THURSDAY 02

FRIDAY 03

SATURDAY 04

SUNDAY 05

SEPTEMBER
WEEK 36

06 MONDAY
LABOR DAY (USA, CAN

07 TUESDAY
ROSH HASHANA (JEWISH NEW YEAR)

Caty farries

08 WEDNESDAY

THURSDAY 09

GANESH CHATURTHI

FRIDAY 10

SATURDAY 11

SUNDAY 12

13 MONDAY

14 TUESDAY

15 WEDNESDAY

SEPTEMBER

YOM KIPPUR (DAY OF ATONEMENT)

THURSDAY 16

FRIDAY 17

SATURDAY 18

SUNDAY 19

SEPTEMBER
WEEK 38

20 MONDAY

21 TUESDAY   FIRST DAY OF SUKKOT

22 WEDNESDAY   SEPTEMBER EQUINOX

THURSDAY 23

FRIDAY 24

SATURDAY 25

SUNDAY 26

SEPTEMBER
WEEK 39

27 MONDAY — HOSHANA RABBAH

28 TUESDAY — SHEMINI ATZERET

29 WEDNESDAY — SIMCHAT TORAH

THURSDAY 30

FRIDAY 01

SATURDAY 02

SUNDAY 03

04 MONDAY
FEAST OF ST FRANCIS OF ASSISI

05 TUESDAY

06 WEDNESDAY

OCTOBER

OCTOBER
WEEK 41

11 MONDAY COLUMBUS DAY (USA); THANKSGIVING DAY (CAN)

12 TUESDAY

13 WEDNESDAY

DUSSEHRA

THURSDAY 14

FRIDAY 15

SATURDAY 16

SUNDAY 17

OCTOBER
WEEK 42

18 MONDAY

19 TUESDAY   MILAD UN NABI (MAWLID)

20 WEDNESDAY

THURSDAY 21

FRIDAY 22

SATURDAY 23

SUNDAY 24

OCTOBER
WEEK 43

25 MONDAY
OCTOBER BANK HOLIDAY (ROI); LABOUR DAY (NZ)

26 TUESDAY

27 WEDNESDAY

THURSDAY 28

FRIDAY 29

SATURDAY 30

BRITISH SUMMER TIME ENDS; HALLOWEEN

SUNDAY 31

NOVEMBER
WEEK 44

01 MONDAY
ALL SAINTS' DAY

02 TUESDAY
ALL SOULS' DAY

03 WEDNESDAY

DIWALI/DEEPAVALI | THURSDAY 04

chloe two challenge start
2 weeks shred
arm : 34cm
thigh : 64cm
waist : 66cm x 79cm ✓

PG :
this workout never worked

GUY FAWKES NIGHT | FRIDAY 05

SATURDAY 06

SUNDAY 07

NOVEMBER
WEEK 45

08 MONDAY

09 TUESDAY

10 WEDNESDAY

VETERANS DAY (USA): REMEMBRANCE DAY (CAN)

THURSDAY 11

FRIDAY 12

SATURDAY 13

REMEMBRANCE SUNDAY

SUNDAY 14

NOVEMBER
WEEK 46

15 MONDAY

16 TUESDAY

17 WEDNESDAY

THURSDAY 18

FRIDAY 19

SATURDAY 20

SUNDAY 21

NOVEMBER
WEEK 47

22 MONDAY

23 TUESDAY

24 WEDNESDAY

NOVEMBER

THANKSGIVING DAY (USA)

THURSDAY 25

FRIDAY 26

SATURDAY 27

FIRST SUNDAY OF ADVENT

SUNDAY 28

NOVEMBER DECEMBER

29 MONDAY   FIRST DAY OF HANUKKAH

30 TUESDAY   ST ANDREW'S DAY (SCOTLAND)

01 WEDNESDAY

THURSDAY 02

FRIDAY 03

SATURDAY 04

SUNDAY 05

DECEMBER
WEEK 49

06 MONDAY
LAST DAY OF HANUKKAH

07 TUESDAY

08 WEDNESDAY
FEAST OF THE IMMACULATE CONCEPTION

THURSDAY 09

FRIDAY 10

SATURDAY 11

SUNDAY 12

13 MONDAY

14 TUESDAY

15 WEDNESDAY

THURSDAY 16

FRIDAY 17

SATURDAY 18

SUNDAY 19

DECEMBER
WEEK 51

20 MONDAY

21 TUESDAY DECEMBER SOLSTICE

22 WEDNESDAY

THURSDAY 23

CHRISTMAS EVE;
CHRISTMAS DAY [SUBSTITUTE DAY] (USA)

FRIDAY 24

CHRISTMAS DAY

SATURDAY 25

BOXING DAY; ST. STEPHEN'S DAY (ROI)

SUNDAY 26

DECEMBER
WEEK 52

27 MONDAY CHRISTMAS DAY [SUBSTITUTE DAY] (UK, CAN, AUS & NZ)

28 TUESDAY BOXING DAY [SUBSTITUTE DAY] (UK, AUS & NZ)

29 WEDNESDAY

THURSDAY   30

NEW YEAR'S EVE;
NEW YEAR'S DAY [SUBSTITUTE DAY] (USA)   FRIDAY   31

NEW YEAR'S DAY   SATURDAY   01

SUNDAY   02

NOTES